CODE BREAKERS

Contents

Simon Cheshire

Story illustrated by
Ned Woodman

Heinemann

In this story

 Harry

 Kate

 Mrs Smith

 Head teacher

Tricky words

- spooky
- messages
- curse
- worse
- ghosts
- proves

Introduce these tricky words and help the reader when they come across them later!

Story starter

Harry and Kate are members of SCARY, a secret club which investigates spooky mysteries. One day, they heard about some spooky messages that were appearing on computer screens at Hillside School.

The Case of the Coded Messages

Harry and Kate went to Hillside School to meet Mrs Smith, the ICT teacher.

"Tell us about the spooky messages," said Harry.

"We want to find out what is really happening," said Kate.

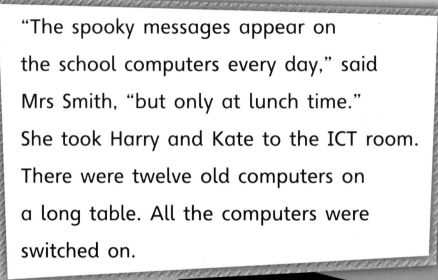

"The spooky messages appear on the school computers every day," said Mrs Smith, "but only at lunch time." She took Harry and Kate to the ICT room. There were twelve old computers on a long table. All the computers were switched on.

Why do the messages only appear at lunch time?

There was a boy sitting at one computer. "Any messages yet?" asked Mrs Smith.

"No," said the boy. "But I've got my notebook ready for when a message does appear."

"Are these computers linked to the Internet?" asked Kate.

"No," said Mrs Smith.

"Mrs Smith!" cried the boy. "Look! It's happening again!"

Everyone looked at the screens.

Rows of random letters flashed up on all the screens. The letters kept stopping and starting for a few seconds. Each time they stopped, they spelled out words:

The dead will walk ...

Secrets from long ago will be told ...

Beware the curse of the wolf ...

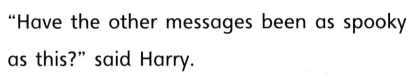

"Have the other messages been as spooky as this?" said Harry.

"Some have been worse," said the boy.

The boy gave Kate his notebook.

He had written down every message.

They were all about ghosts, secrets and dead people.

"These must be coming from ghosts," said Harry.

"Or there's something wrong with the computers," said Kate.

"No," said Mrs Smith. "There's nothing wrong with the computers. They are old but we've had them checked many times."

"Are the computers linked to each other?" asked Kate.

"Yes," said Mrs Smith, "and they're also linked to the computer in the head teacher's room."

"Has the head teacher seen these messages?" asked Harry.

"No," said Mrs Smith. "It's very strange — they always disappear before he gets here."

"That proves they must be sent by ghosts," said Harry.

"Just because we don't know who sent them doesn't mean they have been sent by ghosts," said Kate. "We need to talk to the head teacher."

The head teacher was in his office.

He was using his computer.

It looked very new and very powerful.

"Excuse me," said Kate, "but I think I've worked out why the computers in the ICT room are going wrong. When a new computer is linked to old computers, it can make funny things happen to them." "But why do *spooky* messages appear?" said Harry.

Secrets from Long Ago

by
B A Goodchild

"Oh! I know why," said the head teacher.

"I've been using my new computer every

lunch time – I'm writing a spooky book."

"So that's why the messages stopped when

you went to the ICT room!" said Kate.

"I love spooky stories!" said Harry. "Can I

read it?"

The head teacher printed out a copy

for Harry.

Harry read the story on the bus home. It was a very spooky story. It was full of ghosts, secrets from the past and dead people who walked. But there was nothing about "the curse of the wolf".

Nothing at all.

KATE'S REPORT

The head teacher's new computer was making funny things happen to the old computers.

Some of the text from his spooky stories was sent to the old computers.

The messages were not from ghosts.

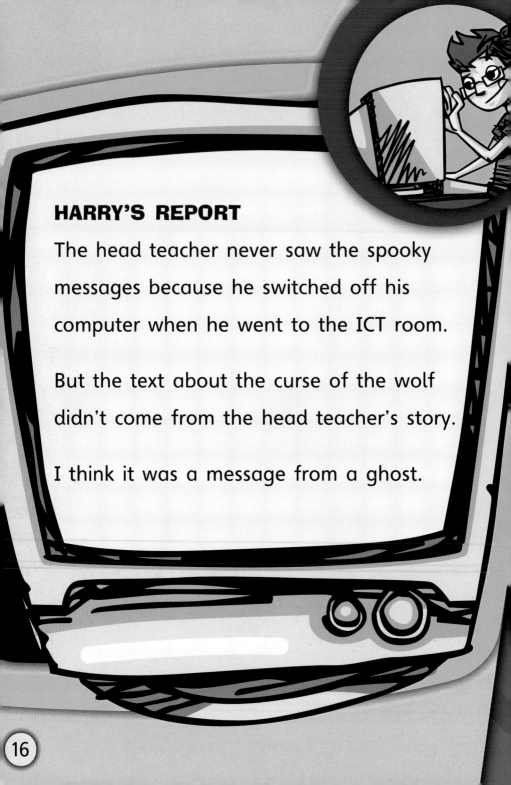

HARRY'S REPORT

The head teacher never saw the spooky messages because he switched off his computer when he went to the ICT room.

But the text about the curse of the wolf didn't come from the head teacher's story.

I think it was a message from a ghost.

Quiz

Text Detective

- Why did the strange messages appear on the school computers?
- Whose report do you think is closest to the truth?

Word Detective

- **Phonic Focus**: Unstressed vowels
  Page 11: Which letters represent the unstressed vowel in 'teacher' and 'computer'? (er)
- Page 3: Find a word meaning 'ghostly'.
- Page 6: Why do the last three sentences end with dots?

Super Speller

Read these words:

appear   starting   computer

Now try to spell them!

HA! HA! HA!

Q Why did the computer sneeze?

A Because it had caught a virus!

17

Find out about

- Writing messages in code

Tricky words

- shaved
- hard-boiled
- special
- secret
- enemies
- Enigma
- Colossus
- data

Introduce these tricky words and help the reader when they come across them later!

Text starter

For hundreds of years, people have used codes to write secret messages that they didn't want other people to read. They changed the letters around or even changed letters for numbers. Then the person who got the message had to decode it!

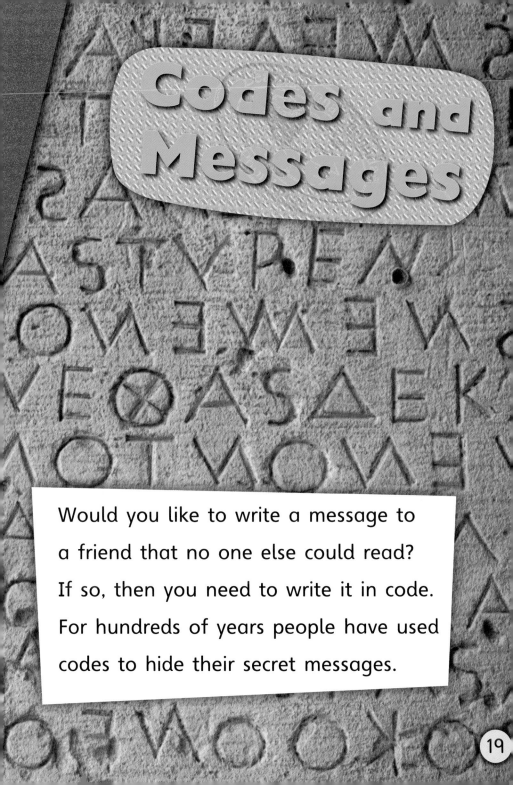

Codes and Messages

Would you like to write a message to a friend that no one else could read? If so, then you need to write it in code. For hundreds of years people have used codes to hide their secret messages.

Hiding messages ... on a head!

Long ago, the Greeks wrote secret messages on the heads of their slaves! First, they shaved all the hair from the head of the slave and then they wrote the message on his shaved head.

When his hair grew again, the message was hidden!

Was this a good way to send a secret
message? No! It was much too slow!
And everyone could read the secret
message until the hair grew again!

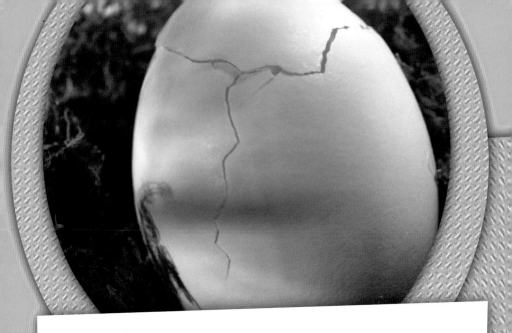

Hiding messages ... on an egg!

Long ago people wrote secret messages
on hard-boiled eggs!

First, they made special ink from vinegar.
Then they wrote their message on the
eggshell. The ink went straight through
the shell, so the message was hidden.
To read the message, the friend had to
take the shell off the egg – and there was
the message on the white of the egg!

Was this a good way to send a secret message? No! You couldn't write much on an eggshell. And what if your friend ate the egg before reading the message?

Famous code-makers

In 1586, Mary Queen of Scots was secretly planning to become Queen of England. She sent letters in code to her friends asking them to help her with her plan. But her letters were decoded by her enemies, and when they found out, they had her head chopped off!

An Italian could read this writing using a mirror!

Leonardo da Vinci was a famous Italian inventor. He didn't want anyone to steal his ideas, so he wrote all his notes in code. He wrote from right to left across the page and wrote all the letters the wrong way round.

It looked like scribble! But you could read it if you looked in a mirror!

War-time codes

In World War Two, the Germans made a machine called "Enigma". They did not want their enemies to know what they were planning.

So Enigma turned their messages into code. To make it more tricky, parts of the code were changed every day!

Enigma means 'tricky puzzle'.

People in England tried very hard to crack the Enigma code. They built a computer called Colossus and worked out the Enigma code.

The Germans did not know that the Enigma code had been cracked. They did not know that their secret messages were not secret any more.

SE not {cup 1 g

Secret codes today

Do people still use codes today? Yes! Anyone who does not want someone else to read their message might use a code.

E{axBreak 0 BC
se fUL{x0 y0 M
m gs rlt cyUL
en fBE{Break a
if n/fBE false
d 0 ne/fUL ed/
findfont/xAsc
ate pop fT3{/e
}if [Sx 0 0 Sy
makefont set

```
{1 sub}if}if/c
{/y1 ed/x1 ed
x1 mul cbStr
tr div exch}if
dxExtra dyExt
dxUL dyUL rmt
```

Lots of data on the Internet uses codes. If you buy something on the Internet, you don't want people knowing where you keep your money or how much money you have got! When you enter your number it only shows as a code, so no one else can read your number.

```
neg xAscent yA
ont [Sx 0 0 S
```

Make your own code!

Can you read this?

NBLF VQ B TFDSFU DPEF

It looks like nonsense! But it is just a simple code. All you need to do is to change each letter for the letter which comes before it in the alphabet!

So ...   N is M

B is A

L is K

F is E

What word have you got?

The word is "MAKE".

Now do the same with the other words and work out the message.

Now you can send secret messages, and your teachers won't know what you have written!

Look at the bottom of the page to find the answer.

MAKE UP A SECRET CODE

Quiz

Text Detective

- How would you read a 'hard-boiled egg' message?
- Who would you like to send a secret message to?

Word Detective

- **Phonic Focus:** Unstressed vowels
  Page 22: Which letters represent the unstressed vowel in 'vinegar'? (ar)
- Page 21: Find a word made from two words.
- Page 27: Find a word meaning 'break'.

Super Speller

Read these words:

friend   asking   until

Now try to spell them!

HA! HA! HA!

Q What is the best hand to write with?

A Neither – it's best to write with a pen!